all color book of Mushrooms
and Fungi by Moira Savonius

Contents

This edition first published 1974 by
Octopus Books Limited
59 Grosvenor Street, London W1
ISBN 0 7064 0315 0

Published in the USA 1974 by
Bounty Books a division of
Crown Publishers Inc
419 Park Avenue South, NY 10016
Title code 514109

previous page: **Lycoperdon perlatum**

opposite: **Peziza aurantia**

Introducing fungi

Fungi span the world and are just as numerous and varied as flowering plants. They range from microscopic organisms to huge solid bodies; from life savers like penicillin, to killers such as ergot; from rusts and mildews which damage growing crops, to the yeasts which have been used since time immemorial in the preparation of food and drink. Fungi of all kinds are of vital importance to Nature's housekeeping. They are the waste disposers, a great company of organisms whose silent and often invisible activities break down and recycle all the organic debris of the world which would otherwise long since have smothered and buried the plants and animals that produced it.

Fungi have been at work since life began on earth. To quote Carlyle: "Nature alone is antique and the oldest art a mushroom". Although they are so varied in size and appearance, all fungi have one thing in common and that is their lack of chlorophyll. Unlike the green plants of the world they cannot utilize sunlight and the carbon dioxide of the air to turn inorganic materials into organic tissue. They must extract their nourishment, like man and animals, from organic materials, and in so doing they destroy or 'eat' whatever they are feeding upon.

In order to survive, fungi must have moisture and oxygen and they thrive best in warm and humid conditions. They are at their most active and destructive in the tropics and many of them can grow perfectly normally in complete darkness such as in cellars, caves and coal mines where they attack and rot the wooden pit props. In the open many fungi grow in dark woods where few green plants can survive in the heavy shade of the trees, but among the numerous species there are also many which need a good light in order to grow and reproduce in a normal way.

When one speaks of fungi, most people understand the word to mean the larger members of this huge group, in other words the mushrooms and 'toadstools', the bracket fungi, the puff balls and the various other often strange and exotic-looking organisms which are big enough to be noticed and recognized fairly easily. What is not generally realized is that these visible and often brightly coloured fungi are not, in themselves, the whole story. They are merely the fruiting bodies, more or less equivalent to the flower clusters of green plants, and a large and important part of the fungus remains hidden in the ground and may not give any visible proof of its presence on the surface for long periods of time. In some cases, as with truffles, even the fruiting bodies never appear above ground and are only found by their smell, which can be detected by specially trained dogs.

Fungi reproduce themselves through minute spores, which are formed in different ways in or on the fruiting body. In the common mushroom and other fungi of the same kind the spores are shed from flanges, known as gills, on the under surface of the fungus cap. In fungi of the *Boletus* type the gills are replaced by a mass of narrow tubes whose pore-like openings are clearly visible. Sometimes the spores are born on little teeth or in wide shallow open pits or sunken bottle-shaped pockets with a minute opening on the surface. In puff balls and allied fungi the ball itself is one large spore container and in the strange Birds' Nest fungi the little 'eggs in the nest' are the spore carriers.

In most fungi the spore production is immense and it has been calculated that in an ordinary mushroom every square millimetre of gill surface can produce about 130,000 spores, which are all discharged in a matter of five or six days. The colouring of the spores varies tremendously in different kinds of fungi and is a great help in identification. If a ripe fungus cap is picked and laid on a piece of white paper, protected from draughts under an inverted bowl, the spores which fall down will produce what is known as a spore print and when a large number have been shed the colour is visible.

Only a small proportion of the spores end up in situations exactly suited to their needs, but when they do they germinate and send out little tubes which elongate into what are known as hyphae. These branch and extend and often join up with similar hyphae produced by other spores which have landed in the same place. When a lot of hyphae have appeared and spread to form a white mass of thin filaments, known as the mycelium, coarser string-like threads are often produced to help the fungus to spread quickly further afield. These may be black or brown, grey or a whitish colour.

It is the mycelium which actually breaks down the dead branches, the old stumps, the rotting leaves, discarded organic rubbish or whatever substance it is growing on, and the fruiting bodies are not formed until the fungus has become well nourished by extracting food from its surroundings. At the right season and under the right conditions of temperature and moisture little knobs appear on the mycelium,

where large numbers of the fine threads grow together into a knot, gradually push towards the surface, and finally appear as mushrooms, toadstools, fairy clubs or some other form of fungus. When they have reached full maturity, spore production starts and can be extremely rapid. From beginning to end the whole process may take no more than eight hours.

Most fungi have a definite odour and quite apart from a kind of general fungus smell which most people can recognize as such, there is a varied range, some fruity, some sweet or spicy, some pleasantly flowery and others downright disgusting, but always difficult to pin down exactly. The smell seems to vary with the sniffer, and a fungus which one person thinks is scented like lilac blossom may seem to another to stink of gas, so the smelling test is not by any means

reliable. But although superficially many fungi seem difficult to distinguish from each other, they do have individual characteristics and anybody really interested can learn to recognize at least the more important kinds quite easily.

Fungus cultivation was well established among ants and termites long before man came upon the scene and primitive forms of fungus culture have been going on among native tribes in the tropics probably since prehistoric times. It is known that the Japanese have grown a certain fungus named *Shii-take* for perhaps as long as 2000 years, inoculating newly cut logs of wood from others already infected and then stacking them in suitable moist and shady places until the fruiting bodies appear and can be gathered. The Chinese have similarly cultivated the Jew's Ear fungus and peasants in France and Italy

have had their own local methods of growing certain edible wood stump fungi. It was not however until early in the seventeenth century that the first attempt at serious commercial mushroom growing began in France. By the end of the century several treatises had been written on the subject and now mushroom growing is big business in many parts of the world. Varieties of the common mushroom are particularly suited to cultivation because the substance they prefer to grow on is well rotted horse manure, which can easily be supplied, and it is not difficult to provide the right conditions for their growth. Most other fungi are not so amenable and because many of them grow only in association with the roots of trees, they cannot be induced to appear anywhere except in woodlands.

Dryad's Saddle (see page 70)

Edible mushrooms

A very large number of fungi are edible, and the general opinion as to whether a certain fungus is fit to eat or not depends very much on the part of the world in which one happens to reside. In Britain most people are highly suspicious of anything but the common mushroom, and the rather tasteless cultivated form at that. On the continent of Europe many more kinds are eaten and the further east and north one goes the more edible fungi are used and appreciated. Nearly 300 different kinds are allowed to be sold in the markets in Sweden, and in Finland, Poland and Russia vast quantities are eaten, especially the Lactarius species, recognized by their milky juice and listed as inedible in many books on fungi. In the United States and Canada where a large number of the inhabitants are descended from European and Scandinavian ancestors, there is still a background knowledge of edible fungi much greater than in Britain, and a new interest is reviving.

The flavour varies a great deal and some fungi are far more palatable than others or make for better eating because their flesh is thick and firm and tender when cooked. The best of these are described in this chapter, but quality is also of great importance and more so in the case of fungi than with most other vegetable foods. It is the nature of the majority of fungi to grow quickly and to decay with equal or even greater speed, and fungi not only rot but are devoured by a great many different insects which feed on the flesh and lay their eggs in it. Once a mushroom or other edible fungus has been attacked in this way it is no longer fit for human consumption.

At first sight it is not always obvious whether or not a fungus is in a suitable state to eat. It may look a fine big specimen without any external blemishes, but if you break the cap in two, or separate the stalk from the top and then notice that there are round holes and meandering burrows in the flesh, that is a sure indication that grubs are already at work. A large fungus of any sort is very seldom in perfect condition although occasionally one may find a parasol mushroom or edible boletus of a fair size which is still quite sound and wholesome. Generally speaking, fungi for food should be gathered while they are still young and unblemished and they should be eaten within six hours. If that is not possible then they should be boiled in slightly salted water, drained and stored in the refrigerator where they will keep for 24 hours or so.

Fungi do not disintegrate or go mushy when boiled and in many instances the flavour is improved by long slow cooking which tends to make a more tasty dish than a quick over-hot session in the frying pan. Fungi are not the most digestible of foods, and some people find they cannot eat them at all without suffering discomfort. This is of course a personal idiosyncrasy but actual allergic reactions to some fungi also occur, as they do with a number of other food stuffs. It is certainly wise to use fungi with some discretion in the kitchen and more as an interesting addition to other foods than as a full meal in themselves. Just like monosodium glutamate, fungi seem to bring out the flavour of other things with which they are served, and they are therefore invaluable when included in casseroles and stews, risottos, macaroni dishes, ratatouilles and egg dishes, or when served as an ingredient in a sauce. They also blend particularly well with ham and bacon.

Before cooking, all fungi should be carefully inspected and cleaned. Some, like the delicious yellow chanterelles, need no more preparation than having the lower tip of the stalk cut off and any leaf litter and grit washed away. Young firm mushrooms can be treated in the same way but in older specimens, where the skin of the cap has become tough, this is best peeled off before cooking. This applies also to those with shaggy caps. If the gills look perfectly sound, even if they have already turned dark as they do in mushrooms, they can be left on, but if they seem to have been nibbled by slugs or you notice insects lurking amongst them, it is best to remove them. This can be done quite easily with a sharp knife. All the boletus fungi have a layer of spongy little tubes on the underside and except in very young specimens, these should be taken off before cooking because their texture is not very pleasant and they make excellent hiding places for all kinds of insect eggs and grubs. The stalks of many fungi tend to be tough, even if the caps are tender, and unless they can be quite easily broken they are best discarded. In most cases they are either very stringy or quite hollow so there is little of edible value in any case. The stalks of the common mushroom, however, can be used for soup when chopped up into small pieces, and the same goes for the thick stalks of young specimens of the edible boletus.

When gathering fungi with a view to eating them, one should always pick the complete stalk as well, easing the fungus out of the soil.

The reason for this is that both the colour and texture of the stalk as well as its entire shape can be an important guide to correct identification. If you know fungi well and can recognize them with certainty at first sight, it is unnecessary to do this, but if you intend to identify them at home with the aid of a book, it makes it much easier and more certain if you have the complete specimen and not only the cap. Some quite small detail such as the absence or presence of a ring round the stalk, or a narrow or swollen base, may easily be the main point of distinction between an edible and a poisonous variety.

Fungi grow in many different places in the countryside. Some prefer open spaces such as meadows and woodland clearings, but the great majority like to grow in association with trees. Different kinds have their own preferences, some being most common in beech woods, others in oak woods and many appearing only in association with conifers. Mixed woodlands generally provide the greatest harvest and the kind of forest consisting of pine, spruce, birch and occasional aspens or poplars which is found in large areas of the North American Continent, in Russia and Scandinavia and also in parts of

Germany and Eastern Europe is particularly rich in fungi.

Wood Blewit (*Tricholoma nudum*) This well known edible fungus is a beautiful lilac colour all over when young, but after a time the top of the smooth, slightly moist cap turns brown, while the gills and stem retain their original colour, though sometimes tinged with brown. The flesh is also violet and does not discolour when broken. It appears rather late in the autumn, growing in woods and parks, always under trees. Cut into pieces and gently cooked in its own juices, then simmered slowly with the addition of butter and thin cream, it makes a delicious dish.

Top left and right
Tawny Grisette (*Amanitopsis fulva*)
Although it is a member of the poisonous Amanita group of fungi, the tawny grisette is perfectly safe to eat and has a good flavour. The young fungus bursts out of an egg-shaped membrane or 'volva' and this remains like a broken cup at the base of the stalk. There is no ring on the pale brown stem which grows about six inches tall, and the cap, which starts off a shiny mahogany brown, later becomes paler, especially round the furrowed edges. It is most common in birch woods on peaty soil and can be found from late spring through to early autumn.

Opposite top
Chanterelle (*Cantharellus cibarius*) One of the best of the edible fungi and very easy to recognize by its uniform rich egg-yolk yellow colour and its pleasant smell of apricots. It grows in woodlands of all kinds from late summer to autumn, usually in groups, and often along the pathways of wood ants. Young specimens are button shaped, but later the margin becomes wavy and the centre depressed. When moist, a chanterelle feels like damp chamois leather. It is hardly ever attacked by insects, and unlike most fungi will keep fresh for several days. Delicious fried in butter or oil, mixed with breadcrumbs.

Opposite below
St George's mushroom (*Tricholoma gambosum*) This is one of the few fungi which appear in spring. It is most common on chalky land, growing in grass on downland pastures and scrub covered hillsides, often in closely packed groups. The rather wavy and often irregularly shaped cap, which may grow to 15 centimetres, (6 inches), is a creamy colour, and so is the thick, often slightly curved stem. The gills are white. The specimen in the picture is a triplet, which is rather unusual. This is an excellent fungus, solid and good, with a pleasant clean smell of new meal.

Top
Field mushroom (*Agaricus campestris*)
The wild field mushroom is a different species from the cultivated form and has a far stronger, better flavour. It grows during late summer in open fields or meadows, particularly in places where horses have been grazing the year before. In a young mushroom, the silky white rounded cap is joined to the short white stalk by a membrane which ruptures as the cap expands, leaving a ring round the stem. This gradually shrivels and disappears. The gills are a delicate pink at first, but darken as the mushroom matures and are finally a very dark brown. The flesh flushes pink when exposed to the air. It is excellent for all culinary purposes.

Left
Horse mushroom (*Agaricus arvense*) This looks like a more robust specimen of the field mushroom, but as it ages the skin of the cap becomes distinctly yellow. There is a lax ring round the white stem and the gills are greyish when young, not pink as in the field mushroom. It is important not to confuse this with the very similar yellow-staining mushroom, *Agaricus xanthodermus*, which is poisonous to some people. The test is to make a cut right at the base of the stalk: if the flesh turns bright yellow the mushroom is the Yellow Stainer and should be discarded.

Opposite top
Parasol mushroom (*Lepiota procea*) This stately mushroom, whose fully expanded, parasol-like cap may measure up to 20 centimetres (8 inches) across, is exciting to find. In season in late summer it is usually discovered in grassy places along the margins of woods or in clearings. The slender stem, reaching forty centimetres in height, is bulbous at the base, carries a fringed double ring and is marked below this with distinct brown scaly streaks. The cap has a clearly defined knob or umbo in the centre. The gills and flesh are white and the flavour rather nutty. It is best to peel the shaggy covering off the cap before cooking.

Opposite below
Shaggy parasol (*Lepiota rhacodes*) Less tall and even more shaggy than the true parasol mushroom, this fine fungus is distinguished by a plain dirty-white stem and by the fact that the flesh turns a pinkish-yellow when the cap is cut or broken. The umbo is very dark and glossy and the double ring on the stem is free and can be twisted round. The shaggy parasol prefers rich ground and is more of a woodland species than the true parasol. Occasionally it is found in coniferous woods growing on active wood ant nests. It makes very good eating and can be prepared in any number of ways, after removing the shaggy skin.

Left
Morel (*Morchella esculenta*) Another spring fungus, but of a totally different appearance, the morel can be found in meadows and in woodland clearings and parks during late spring. The fungus is quite hollow and rather brittle, the creamy white stem especially so. The cap is yellowish brown and slightly pointed, and the surface is divided up into alternate ridges and irregular hollows in which the spores are formed. The cap is joined to the stem. Another closely related species, '*Morchella vulgaris*', is very similar but has a more conical cap. Both are delicious and best served in a creamy sauce.

Below
Russula cyamoxantha Growing more often under beeches than in oak woods, this fungus varies from blue-green to violet-purple and the photograph shows this very well. The gills, which feel curiously oily and elastic to the touch, are white and so is the stem, although it may occasionally have a faint purplish tinge. The flesh is firm and white, but under the skin of the cap it is slightly reddish. One of the best of the *Russulas,* with a mild and agreeable taste.

Opposite
Edible boletus (*Boletus edulis*) On the continent of Europe this fungus is known as Cepe, or Steinpiltz, and the term 'Stone fungus' is also used throughout Scandinavia. Next to the field mushroom this is the most nourishing of all the edible fungi and was already much appreciated by the Romans. It is the main ingredient of several brands of packeted mushroom soups. When young it closely resembles a nicely baked brown bun on a stalk. Later, the cap thickens and extends and the layer of dull greeny-yellow tubes on the under surface, which should be removed before it is eaten, becomes more spongy. It appears in mixed woodlands during the autumn.

Below
Birch boletus (*Boletus testaceoscaber*)
Almost as good as *Boletus edulis*, this can
be recognized by its much brighter,
orange-brown cap and the rather more
slender stalk, which is covered in small
black scales. It grows in birch and conifer
woods, first appearing in mid-summer and
going on until early autumn. The pore
surface on the underside is a dirty
greyish-brown colour. When cut or
broken, the flesh gradually turns lilac or
slate-blue, but this may not be apparent
for ten minutes or so. Good to eat either
fried with bacon, tomatoes and onion or
made into soup, added to rice dishes or
omelettes.

Opposite top left
Boletus badius This is more of a 'sticky
bun' than *Boletus edulis*, because the
covering of the cap is shiny chestnut-
brown and rather viscid in young
specimens. The tubes are creamy at first,
later turn yellow and finally have a
greenish tinge. The stalk is fairly slender
and light streaky brown. When bruised,
the tubes turn green and the flesh, which
is yellow, becomes light blue on exposure
to air. This is a common fungus in conifer
woods during late summer, and although
inferior to *Boletus edulis* in flavour, it is
still in the top class for all culinary
purposes.

Opposite top right
Shaggy Cap or Lawyers Wig (*Coprinus
comatus*) Quite unmistakable, with its
narrow cylindrical heads pushing up,
covered in soft almost overlapping shaggy
scales, pure white at first but soon tinted
with ochre, this quick-maturing fungus is
often found in clusters growing in fields
and gardens, by compost or rubbish
heaps or on the roadside where the soil
has been disturbed. The gills start off by
being white, then turn pink, purple, and
black and finally dissolve in a black inky
fluid which has also given the fungus the
name of Ink Cap. When young, while the
gills are still white or pink, it is edible and
has a very delicate taste.

Opposite below
The Shaggy Mushroom (*Agaricus
augustus*) The cap of this very sturdy
fungus is not unlike that of the parasol
mushroom, but it lacks the prominent
umbo in the centre and the scales are
smaller and of a paler rusty brown. In
young unexpanded specimens there are a
few scales on the stem below the ring,
but these drop off later, leaving the stem
white and clean, with a floppy ring
hanging down below the cap. The gills are
white at first and later become brownish.
This is a woodland fungus, growing
during late summer both under conifers
and deciduous trees. It smells distinctly
of anise and is very tasty when cooked.

More edible mushrooms

Walking through autumn woodlands with a basket in search of edible fungi is a very pleasant weekend pastime, and even if one fails to find many of the finest varieties described in the previous chapter, there are many others which, although not of the highest table quality, are nevertheless palatable. The wild harvest which they provide has been of immense value in many parts of the world, especially in eastern and northern Europe and Russia where a severe climate has always made vegetable foods, apart from grain, a scarce commodity during the winter. Nowadays, when deep freezing and canning have revolutionized catering all over the world, fungi, dried or preserved in brine, are not as important as they used to be. They are, however, still collected because people like them and it is always gratifying to get something that is edible and good without having to pay for it!

When Charles Darwin made his famous voyage on the 'Beagle', he discovered that apart from meat and fish the natives of Tierra del Fuego, who wore practically no clothes and seemed amazingly insensitive to cold, ate only two kinds of vegetable foods, berries from the strawberry trees and a certain fungus growing on the southern beech trees, which was later named after him: *Cyttaria darwinii*. Primitive tribes in other parts of the world also rely to a great extent on fungi, and during wars and famines fungus eating has saved the lives of a great many people in Europe who would otherwise have starved to death.

Like the average vegetable, fungi contain a high proportion of water, often almost 90%. This is given off in cooking, so most fungi shrink a great deal: a basketful may yield only a small dish in the end. In the final analysis they have pretty well the same food value as root vegetables, the common mushroom and *Boletus edulis* containing the highest proportion of protein. As one might expect from its colour, the Chanterelle is rich in carotine, which is a source of Vitamin A, and also contains a fair amount of Vitamin D, which prevents rickets in children. This is also found in *Boletus edulis*, in the morel and in the common mushroom, especially the wild field mushroom which grows in a good light. The cultivated mushroom, grown in darkness, is much less valuable in this respect. Little research of this kind has been done so far, but it is well known that yeast, one of the primitive fungi, contains very nearly all known vitamins, which explains its tonic properties.

Religious customs have often had an important effect on the eating habits of nations and in those areas of Eastern Europe where the Greek Orthodox Church decreed periods of fasting in pre-Communist days, fungi assumed an added importance in places where fish was not always easily obtainable. This is one of the reasons why in Russia and the countries adjoining, fungi have been used more widely than anywhere else and many ways of cooking them have been devised. In Karelia, on the borders of Finland and Russia, *Lactarius torminosus* is prepared in the following most delicious way. The fungi are cleaned and the furry pink skin is removed. They are then boiled in salted water for ten minutes, rinsed and drained. When they are cold, they are chopped up finely and mixed with a little chopped raw onion, thick cream, which may be either fresh or sour according to taste, salt, pepper and a dash of vinegar, and served at the start of a meal or as an accompaniment to cold meat.

Russulas are sometimes boiled and drained, then dipped in batter and fried crisp in deep fat, or they may be used as a base on which to pile a mound of minced bacon and chicken liver mixed with raw egg, then baked in the oven until the meat mixture is cooked through. Fungi can be salted down for future use quite simply by first boiling them and then packing them down in jars with a good sprinkling of coarse salt between the layers. Before using, they should be well washed to remove as much of the salt as possible and the dish to which they are added will probably need no further salting. They can also be bottled, and again should be briefly boiled first and then packed into preserving jars and covered in acidified brine, made by dissolving 1½ oz. of salt and 2½ fl. oz. (¼ cup) of lemon juice in 4 pints (10 cups) of water. Rubber bands and covers are fixed on the jars and they should be sterilized in a pressure cooker at 10 lb. pressure for 40 minutes.

Although the vast majority of fungi are non-poisonous comparatively few of the many thousands of known species have any culinary value. Many are either extremely tough and need more chewing than modern man is willing or able to give, or they are so small and fragile that when they are cooked and the water has disappeared, very little solid matter remains. Some have an unpleasant taste and although they may not be harmful, one must be starving indeed to eat willingly something that is really unpalatable. Many fungi which are acrid in a raw state and likely to cause

severe indigestion if eaten become quite mild when boiled in water. This applies especially to the *Lactarius* species and also to certain *Russulas*, and a preliminary boiling of all fungi apart from Chanterelles, mushrooms and parasol fungi, and *Boletus edulis*, is always advisable,

before they are served.

Horn of Plenty (*Craterellus cornucopioides*) Found mainly in beech woods from late summer through to autumn, this strange dark fungus does not look very appetizing but is nevertheless both edible and good. Shaped like a small trumpet with a split and wavy margin, it

is dark blackish-brown on the inner surface and a paler greyish colour on the outside. In France it is known as 'The Trumpet of the Dead' but this obviously refers only to its appearance and not to any deadly qualities. It blends very well in casserole dishes and risottos and, because the flesh is thin, it can be easily dried and stored to be used as flavouring.

Left
Mitrophora semi-libera A relative of the morel, growing in moist woodlands on rich soil, this rather insubstantial fungus has a cap which merely sits on top of the white stalk without being attached to it. Another allied species, *Morchella conica*, slightly more robust and with a darker brown cone-shaped cap and a yellowish stalk, grows both in deciduous woods and in conifer plantations, but neither of these is common. Both are edible if treated in the same way as the morel.

Below
Edible Stump Fungus (*Pholiota mutabilis*) Many fungi spring from old tree stumps but few of them are edible. This is an exception and invariably grows in a crowded mass, with the wavy, more or less flattened caps reaching six centimetres (2½ inches) across. The thin stalks are surrounded by a membraneous ring and become darker towards the base. When moist, the caps are a rich date-brown in colour, but as they dry they become lighter in the centre. The gills on the underside are cinnamon coloured. Although it is rather lacking in substance, it makes a worthwhile addition to savoury stews, adding, as it does, both flavour and colour.

Opposite
Honey Fungus (*Armillaria mellea*) The honey fungus normally grows in a mass, either on a rotting old stump or at the base of a living tree. When young the caps are a golden brown, covered in projecting scales, but later these wear off and the colour becomes paler. The gills are creamy-coloured at first, but later turn light brown and spotted. The stem has a white ring spotted with yellow, near the top, and below this it is darkly honey-coloured and hairy, somewhat swollen towards the base. The flesh is white with a peculiar smell and tastes slightly bitter when raw. This will disappear on boiling and the honey fungus is safe to eat, but not particularly well flavoured.

Above
Fairy Ring Champignon (*Marasmius oreades*) This is only one of the many fungi which grow in circles, killing and discolouring the grass. We no longer believe that these rings are made by dancing fairies, witches or lightning, and although the champignon can ruin a lawn, it is at least edible and tasty. If a good crop appears in summer or autumn, the caps can be threaded on string and hung from the kitchen ceiling to dry for future use. A handful added to stews and casseroles, or chopped up in a vegetable soup, will give a pleasant mushroom flavour. The caps are pale brown, but almost buff when dry, with a raised bump or 'umbo' in the centre. The gills are well spaced and alternately long and short, the thin stalks remarkably tough and hairy at the base.

Opposite top
Sparassis crispa Strangely enough this fungus has no popular name. It might well be called the bath sponge fungus, because this is what it closely resembles from a distance when you see it nestling at the base of a pine tree, where it is most usually found in early autumn. The creamy flesh, divided into countless flattened lobes, is very brittle, and full-grown specimens may grow to 30 centimetres (1 foot) across. The taste is mild and the fungus makes a good soup, or flavouring for an omelette or souffle.

Opposite below left
Giant Puff Ball (*Lycoperdon giganteum*) Potentially the largest of all fungi, this may occasionally grow as big as a sheep, but is usually no more than football size. It appears in pasture land and on road sides in late summer. The white skin is at first downy and then becomes smooth, like kid leather. Gathered young, when the flesh is still white and firm, it can be cut in slices, dipped in egg and breadcrumbs, and fried to provide a nourishing but not very exciting dish. A mature puff ball, filled with billions of brown spores, is useless except as tinder.

Opposite below right
Poor Man's Beef Steak (*Fistulina hepatica*) This extraordinary fungus, looking rather like a large red tongue, grows on living trees, usually sweet chestnut or oak. It is harmless and edible but unfortunately provides only a very poor imitation of an inferior piece of stewing steak. The under surface is covered in a layer of short yellow tubes, which are best removed before cooking. When broken, the flesh exudes a red juice. Beef steak fungus should be boiled and well flavoured with onion or garlic, herbs and spices to make it palatable.

22

Below
Hygrophorus coccineus The blood red or bright scarlet cap of this small fungus is only 2-5 centimetres (1-2 inches). It starts off by being somewhat bell-shaped, and later becomes almost flat, while the colour fades to orange and yellow. The gills are yellow with a red flush and the stalk is the same colour as the cap at the top, becoming paler towards the base. It grows in grassy places, very often round the edges of woods, from early summer until late in the autumn. Boiled or fried and added to rice dishes it gives colour and flavour.

Opposite top left and right
Wood hedgehog fungus (*Hydnum rufescens*) Both this fungus and the allied *Hydnum repandum* are strictly autumnal woodland fungi, more common in the northern mixed woodlands than in the south. They are easily identified by the fact that they do not have gills or tubes on the under surface, but instead a layer of small teeth or blunt spines. They usually grow in groups or rings and the pale buff *Hydnum repandum*, which often becomes rather lopsided and distorted, can reach a large size, while *Hydnum rufescens* is smaller and foxy-brown in colour. A third species, *Sarcodon imbricatum*, which is only found in coniferous woods on sandy soil, has a grey brown scaly cap and grey teeth and stem. All three are edible, but are best if boiled first to remove the slightly acrid taste and then dipped in breadcrumbs, fried, and served with fried onions.

Opposite below
Cortinarius albo-violaceus This interesting autumn fungus of beech and oak woods can be recognized by the very pale lilac-blue colouring of the cap and top of the club-shaped stalk, while the lower half appears to be wearing a white 'stocking'. When young, the cap and the stalk are joined by thin cobwebby strands. When full grown and more or less flattened, the cap always has a prominent hump in the middle, giving it the shape of a hat. The gills, which are set rather far apart, are also pale violet at first, but later become cinnamon-brown. The rather thick flesh has a slight tinge of violet. The flavour is mild.

Below
Jew's Ear *(Auricularia auricula)* In Europe
this peculiar fungus grows almost
exclusively on elder, but in North
America it is found on many different
deciduous trees. The colour varies from a
rather dull flesh tint to a very dark brown.
The flesh is thin and translucent and
when moist it feels like soft rubber but
becomes quite hard on drying. The shape
is like a very irregular shallow saucer with
the inner surface shiny and the outer
slightly velvety and greyish. Young, light-
coloured specimens can be eaten, and in
China a close relative of this fungus,
Auricularia polytricha, is cultivated on
cut oak saplings.

Opposite
Oyster mushroom *(Pleurotus ostreatus)*
This late autumn and winter fungus which
grows on beech trees, causing a damaging
rot, is a beautiful blue-grey colour when
young, but gradually changes to brown as
it ages. The whitish yellow gills extend
down the short stalk, which is always set
on one side of the cap. The individual
specimens often grow in layers on top of
each other. While still young and blue the
Oyster mushroom is edible and good and
it can easily be dried above a stove or in
a warm room for storing. It should be
cooked gently and served in a thick
creamy sauce.

Above

Russula atropurpurea The *Russulas* are an enormous family of fungi, numbering well over a hundred species. They are typical woodlanders, appearing in late summer and are often very brightly coloured. They are quickly attacked by slugs, snails and insects of various sorts and it is not easy to find perfect healthy specimens. Many of them have a very bitter, acrid or peppery taste, but this one, recognized by its purplish-red cap which is almost black in the centre, is mild tasting and pleasant when mature, although very young specimens may be a little bitter.

Opposite top

Russula vesca In this *Russula* the colour of the cap is very variable, ranging from a dull reddish-brown to a buff pink like that of the specimen in the photograph. When the cap flattens out in maturity, the skin on the top often pulls back from the edge, revealing the flesh along the margin. The gills, as in most *Russulas*, are white, but become slightly spotted with brown as the fungus ages, and the firm flesh slowly discolours to a pale brown when broken. It is most common in oak woods and has a pleasantly nutty flavour, blending well with egg dishes of all kinds.

Opposite below left

Russula nitida This is a rather small and slender fungus with a cap that quickly becomes flat and depressed in the centre. The colour is at first wine red, but later fades near the margin, leaving the middle still fairly dark. There are distinct radiating grooves along the edge of the cap and the gills are creamy-yellow. The stalk swells a little towards the base and is often shaded with pink. It is most commonly found in birch woods and is good to eat. The best way to decide whether or not a *Russula* is edible is to taste a small piece of the uncooked flesh. Only those with a mild, bland taste should be used.

Opposite below right

Coprinus atramentarius This rather unattractive-looking, bell-shaped fungus is a close relative of the Lawyer's Wig but does not 'autodigest' or dissolve in the same way, although the gills do turn black with age. It is mainly a woodland fungus, often clustering close to deciduous trees, but it also appears from time to time in gardens or round the edges of fields, any time from mid-summer to late autumn. It is edible, but will cause sickness and frightening purple blotches on the face and arms if served with wine, beer or spirits because it contains 'antabuse', sometimes administered to alcoholics to try and wean them from drink.

Above
Boletus scaber The picture shows a very unusual 'Siamese twin' specimen of this common birchwood fungus. The colour of the cap varies from grey-brown to dark brown and it is rather sticky to the touch. The tubes are a dirty grey and become blotchy when bruised. The whole fungus feels very soft and rather unpleasantly spongy and should only be gathered when it is quite young and the cap still rounded. It is much attacked by insects and the flesh contains a very high proportion of water.

Opposite top
Saffron milk cap (*Lactarius deliciousus*)
All the members of the genus *Lactarius*

exude a milky juice when cut and in this case it is a rich saffron yellow in colour and soon turns orange. The cap is often distinctly banded with greenish rings, the centre may be depressed on a mature specimen, and the edge slightly wavy. The gills are orange and turn green if bruised. It is very difficult indeed to find a specimen which is not riddled with insect maggots even at an early stage. It grows in coniferous woods, often in groups and should be thoroughly washed before cooking to remove as much as possible of the milk.

Opposite below
Clitocybe nebularis Another woodland fungus, more often found under conifers

than deciduous trees. It appears after late summer and early autumn rains, pushing up its smooth grey rounded caps, which later become almost flat, or even slightly hollow in the centre. The whole fungus is very solid and fleshy, with a stout stem thickening further towards the base. The gills are crowded together, white at first, then pale grey with a yellow tinge. The flesh is white and soft and has a rather sweet smell. Pleasant to eat but hard on the digestion, so a little is better than too much. It should always be boiled in water for a few minutes before use.

Above
Woolly milk cap (*Lactarius torminosus*)
This is one of the most attractive of all
the fungi, with its delicate pink colouring
and the soft furry top which curls under
at the edges. In a mature specimen there
are clear concentric rings of lighter and
darker pink on the cap, which is
depressed in the middle. Many people
consider it inedible, but in Eastern
Europe, Russia and especially in Finland
it is the most popular of all fungi. The
white milky juice has a strong peppery
taste, but this disappears when the
fungus is boiled and rinsed, which it
always should be before using.
Common in coniferous woods in autumn.

Opposite left
Lactarius vellereus Another member of
the same family, but pure white instead
of pink, with a soft velvety cap which is
always curled down at the edges. The
stem tends to be short and stout and the
gills, which are set wide apart, are white
when young and then turn dull yellow.
In older specimens the cap is slightly
stained with brown, especially in the
depression at the centre. The profuse milk
is white and peppery but after boiling and
rinsing the taste becomes mild and the
fungus is perfectly safe and pleasant to
eat. It is found in woodlands in autumn
and is more common in the north.

Opposite right
Lactarius mitissimus This is a rather small
and fragile fungus always growing under
conifers. The top of the cap is more or
less orange-red with a small knob in the
centre, the gills are pinkish-ochre and the
stem is the same colour as the cap. The
white milk is only slightly bitter. It needs
the same treatment as the other two
mentioned above, and this applies to
nearly all the *Lactarius* fungi. None of
them are poisonous, but in some cases
the extreme peppery or bitter taste is not
completely removed by boiling. (See
Lactarius rufus, page 52).

Poisonous fungi

There are comparatively few poisonous fungi and even fewer that are really deadly. Among the 30,000 or so different fungi distributed throughout the world, of a size that might invite picking for food, less than one per cent are killers, which is a much smaller proportion than among the flowering plants. Deaths caused by fungus eating are, in the great majority of cases, due to three closely related species, all members of the genus *Amanita*. The reason why this happens is because people mistake them for the common mushroom, although there are quite distinct differences. If fungus pickers were looking for more exotic things instead, like chanterelles, *boletus*, wood blewits or hedgehog fungi there would be practically no danger, because none of these even remotely resembles *Amanitas*. The widespread notion that only field mushrooms are fit to eat, is in fact more dangerous if accompanied by ignorance, than a more general acceptance of the existence of many kinds of edible fungi.

The *Amanitas* contain several different very dangerous toxins. Some of these are destroyed by cooking, but others are not, so it is folly to think that any fungus can be eaten if it has been boiled. The most dangerous thing about *Amanita* toxin is that it is slow acting and no symptoms appear for about twelve hours, when it is too late to use a stomach pump. Once the poison begins to act it rapidly destroys the liver and kidneys, causes heart failure and internal bleeding, and although death within a few days is not inevitable, severe damage to the organs is caused. The poison is so strong that very little is needed and a single small specimen of one of these deadly fungi included in a dish is quite enough to be fatal. A serum is produced by the Pasteur Institute in France and can be the means of saving a life, but there is no known antidote.

The two most dangerous, and strangely enough most innocent looking, of the *Amanitas* are *Amanita virosa*, the Destroying Angel, and *Amanita verna*. Happily neither of them are common, although they grow in woodlands both in Britain and Europe as well as in North America. The Destroying Angel is pure white all over, and has no distinctive smell or taste. It grows out of a membraneous covering which remains as a cup at the base of the shaggy stalk. The stem is ringed, and the cap, which is perfectly smooth and shining and slightly sticky to the touch, is often lop-sided. The gills are permanently white. *Amanita verna* is very like the Deathcap mushroom in size and shape, but the cap is usually quite white, sometimes slightly tinged with brown at the centre. It has a very slender white stem.

The poison of the brightly coloured Fly Agaric is less dangerous, usually producing nothing worse than temporary sickness and a kind of intoxicated madness, followed by a coma which appears to obliterate all memory of what has happened. There have been cases of people suffering from this poisoning waking up to find themselves in a mental hospital and wondering how on earth they came to be there. At one time it was suggested that the Vikings might have eaten the Fly Agaric to induce the mad frenzy which characterized their fighting, but modern historians no longer believe this story. It is, however, well known that certain primitive tribes in eastern Siberia have used the fungus as an intoxicant. The poison it contains is rather similar to that of the deadly nightshade and is certainly dangerous if taken in too large a quantity.

There is an interesting wall painting in an old chapel at Plaincourault in France, depicting the Tree of Knowledge in the shape of a group of Fly Agarics, with Eve beside it, looking very uncomfortable and clutching her stomach after, presumably, already having eaten of the fruit. It was painted at the end of the thirteenth century and may well have been intended as a warning to the local inhabitants not to try and gain forbidden knowledge by experimenting with the red and white toadstools growing wild in the woods.

When the Spaniards conquered Mexico in 1522, they discovered that the Aztecs used a certain fungus as a narcotic. The Indians were unwilling to reveal the true nature of this 'sacred' mushroom, but one of the Spanish priests who went out to Mexico a few years later managed to find out and wrote a description of a gathering he had attended, where the little black fungus which the Indians called 'nanacatl' was eaten with honey and caused intoxication and hallucinations. He naturally objected very strongly to this habit and all the Catholic priests sent to Mexico by the Spanish government tried to stamp it out, but seemingly to no avail, because the mushrooms are used by Mexican Indians today.

Mankind still clings to the mistaken belief that hallucinations produced by drugs of one kind and another will reveal the secrets of existence, when in fact they do nothing of the kind. A more or less poisoned body merely causes confusion of the mind and 'revelations' of this sort are dubious.

There are three quite small, fragile looking fungi of the genus *Inocybe* which are poisonous. They are all woodland species and two of them have pale lilac stalks while the third is a little nondescript tobacco-brown fungus with a short stalk which tapers downwards. Another small fungus, *Clitocybe rivulosa*, often grows in grass and on lawns, in rings and groups, and has at times been confused with the Fairy ring mushroom with dire results. It is paler in colour, the cap is quite flat or depressed in the centre and the gills are crowded together instead of being spaced well apart. The very similar but almost white *Clitocybe dealbata*, which also grows in grass, is equally poisonous and there are a few more little members of the tribe, some of them growing in woodlands, that should on no account be eaten. Tiny fungi should preferably not be gathered at all. Even the harmless ones are in any case so lacking in flesh that they are worthless as food. Fungi with caps that split at the margins should also be avoided because several poisonous varieties have this habit. One of them, *Rhodophyllus sinuatus*, also known as *Entoloma lividum*, often causes trouble in France, where people are apt to mistake it for a large mushroom, which it does resemble to some extent, although it has no ring round the stem and the gills are yellow when young and a salmon pink instead of brown when the fungus is mature. Another difference is that it grows in woods, especially under beeches, whereas the mushroom grows in the open.

Poisonous fungi cannot be recognized by any special smell or even by their taste. They do not stain silver spoons black or advertize their poisonous properties in any obvious way so there is no short cut to recognition. In fact they often look deceptively harmless and may even have a pleasant smell. To be completely safe, one must learn to recognize them by studying pic-tures and specimens and avoiding anything which bears a resemblance to a dangerous type. Some of the *Amanitas* are quite harmless but there is a family likeness within the group, so it is safer not to risk danger and to leave them all alone.

Fly Agaric (*Amanita muscaria*) The poisonous Fly Agaric is so often pictured in story books for children that its unmistakable appearance is very familiar to most people. It is a beautiful fungus, most common on poor soils under pines and birches, often growing in quite large groups. The taste is disgusting, and although it is very seldom fatal, it has a strongly poisonous effect if eaten, causing sickness and diarrhoea, hallucinations, convulsions and coma. In many European countries it has in the past been widely used as a fly poison, and some primitive Asiatic tribes have employed it regularly as an intoxicant.

Above

Inocybe patouillardii In its young stage this very dangerous fungus has on occasion been mistaken for a common mushroom, with fatal results, but there are quite distinct differences. Although about the same size, it has no ring on the stalk, and it normally grows close to trees, especially beeches, rather than in the open meadows where mushrooms are found. The cap is bell shaped at first, and more or less white in colour, with silky fibres. Later it expands, but there is always a distinct boss in the centre. The edge often splits and the colour becomes yellowish or even reddish brown. The gills, which are pinkish at first, become a dull olive-yellow. Any part of the fungus which is bruised or wounded quickly develops a red stain and the flesh has an unpleasant rank smell. The fungus may be found any time from early summer to the beginning of autumn.

Opposite top and below

Amanita rubescens and Amanita excelsa These two rather similar fungi, both about the same size as the Fly Agaric, have stems slightly swollen at the base and a lax ring below the cap. *Amanita rubescens*, also known as The Blusher, stains pink if bruised or cut. They are both harmless, but it is unwise to gather them for food, because they can so easily be confused with the somewhat smaller *Amanita pantherina*, the Panther Cap, which is very poisonous indeed, and has even been fatal. On occasions the Panther Cap may grow to 15 centimetres (6 inches). The smoky-brown cap is spattered with white warts, but these can be washed off by rain. Rounded at first, it soon becomes flat and radial lines show at the edge. The gills are white and so is the stem, which is also distinctly swollen at the base. There is a smooth ring round the stem, and below this, hoop-like remnants of the original enveloping membrane can usually be seen. All three fungi grow in woodlands during the summer, but the Panther Cap is more likely to be found in association with beech trees than the other two.

Below
Death Cap *(Amanita phalloides)* This deadly poisonous fungus is not uncommon in beech and oak woods in summer and early autumn, and often several are found growing together. Young specimens are completely enclosed in a white, egg-shaped membrane, which ruptures as they grow. The remains, in the shape of a tattered 'cup' can be seen at the base of the stem, which is also encircled by a rather floppy white ring. The cap is slightly slimy, rounded at first, then almost flat, and a pale yellowish-olive in colour, or occasionally almost white. Both the gills and the stalk are white and do not change colour. When mature, the fungus has a distinctly unpleasant smell.

Opposite top
False Death Cap *(Amanita citrina)* There are two distinct forms of this fungus, one pure white as in the photograph, the other tinted with lemon yellow, with loose white patches on the cap. The narrow white stalk rises from a prominent basal 'bulb' with a circular groove, like a ditch, round the top. There is also a ring round the stem. Neither of the two varieties is poisonous, but the taste is nasty, and because it may so easily be confused with both the Destroying Angel and the Death Cap, *Amanita citrina* should never be gathered for food.

Opposite below
Gyromitra esculenta This odd looking fungus, closely resembling a brown 'brain' perched on a white stalk, is a relation of the morels and, like them, it appears in the spring. It is known to be poisonous, and yet in Eastern Europe and in Sweden and Finland it is eagerly sought and marketed in large quantities because of its superlative taste. The poison, known as gyromitrin, is destroyed if the fungus is dried in the sun and then stored for two or three months before using. It is also soluble in water and after a preliminary boiling for five or six minutes and then a thorough rinsing, the fresh fungi are safe to eat, but they should never be consumed in large quantities because small traces of poison still left may build up in the liver and cause trouble. Individual reaction to morels varies widely and some strains of the fungus, especially in central Europe, appear to be more poisonous than those growing further north. *Gyromitra* is rare in Britain but occurs in North America and is common in Sweden and Finland where it grows profusely in the extensive pine forests on sandy soil.

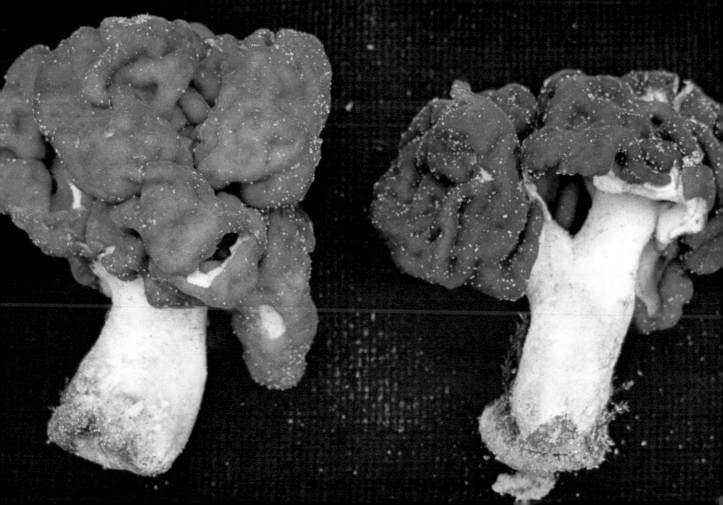

Toadstools

The so-called toadstools have always fascinated and intrigued people. The way they suddenly appear and disappear, often in huge numbers, is mysterious in itself and the enormous variety of different shapes and colours has always appealed to those with artistic imagination. Tales of trolls and fairy magic and the secrets of the forests, which once covered most of Europe, still exert an influence even if they are no longer believed. The knowledge that some fungi are poisonous adds an exciting spice of danger to fungus lore.

Many fungi are undoubtedly beautiful, slender-stalked with caps that remind one of parasols or umbrellas, hats of different styles or possibly wigs. They are often decorated in infinitely delicate detail with tiny glistening particles, fine pleats, soft hairs, scales and granules which may only last in perfection for a very short time. Others are more curious than lovely and in old age, when they begin to sag and collapse, they can sometimes even be repulsive, but they are never dull.

The way they grow and especially the habit many species have of forming rings puzzled early naturalists for centuries, but was finally understood and explained. As the mycelium of these fungi grows in the soil, it exhausts the supply of nutrients it needs, and in order to survive it must move outwards from its starting point. If weather conditions are right a crop of fruiting bodies appears and every year the diameter of the circle increases, until it finally becomes so large that the scattered groups of fungi no longer seem to be growing in a ring but in a curving band.

The grass at the periphery of the circle is often quite distinctly darker green than within it, because the mycelium which is active in that area makes available certain nutrients which improve the growth of grass, while inside the circle conditions are less favourable. In rings formed by the Fairy Ring Champignon the centre is often quite bare because all the air spaces between the soil particles have been filled with the white mycelium threads of the fungus and this prevents rain from penetrating so that the vegetation dies from lack of moisture. Later, as the fungus advances further, the central bare patch will recover and become green again, while other bare areas appear nearer the edge.

Aerial photographs often show fairy rings much more distinctly than they can be seen from ground level. A picture taken over Stonehenge, in Wiltshire, England, shows a number of fairy rings, some very large and all clearly visible. The rings increase in diameter each year and when the annual growth rate is more or less stable it is possible to calculate the age of a ring by its size. Some of them are reckoned to be several hundred years old.

The common honey fungus which occurs pretty well all over the world has the ability to make the timber it attacks luminous. An eerie green glow seen in the woods at night was no doubt familiar even to the cave men and has given rise to many a spooky tale. Old stumps, roots and fallen timber infected with the mycelium of honey fungus are clearly luminous as long as they are damp and the mycelium remains alive. If you bring the wood indoors and it dries out the glow soon disappears. To country dwellers this luminosity is fairly familiar, but those who have spent most of their lives in towns have usually never even heard of it and find it very uncanny.

The fruiting body of the honey fungus does not itself produce any light, but there are other kinds, like the well known Jack o' Lantern in North America, which may be the same thing as *Pleurotus olearius*, a relative of the oyster fungus, growing in the Mediterranean area mainly on the roots of olive trees and oaks. It gives off such a strong light that one can quite easily see to pick it in the dark. Many tropical fungi shine quite brightly at night and a time exposure will give a clear photograph. Most of them grow on tree trunks and the effect of trees 'lit up' in the darkness is often quite startling to strangers who have not seen it before.

Several of the *Mycena* species, with their bell-shaped caps, are also luminous to some extent, although the appearance of the light is rather erratic and brief. Many of them grow on fallen leaves and their presence can cause the leaves to emit a faint light when they are coated with strands of mycelium, and small luminous patches also appear from time to time on the gills or stems of the little fungi themselves. The colour of fungus light varies from white, through yellowish-green to blue-green. Experiments have shown that it is produced only when oxygen is present and the temperature must be at least a couple of degrees above zero centigrade. A stronger light appears if it is warmer. The substance which actually produces the glow is probably similar to luciferin, found in glow worms and other luminous creatures.

Toadstools are very erratic in their appearance, and although the underground mycelia of many of the larger species are perennial, this

does not mean that the fruiting bodies will appear every season. They are certainly likely to come up, and people who regularly gather fungi get to know where to look for them, but one can never be sure, and sometimes several years may pass without a sign of them if the weather conditions have not been just right for their development.

It is impossible to tell what is going on beneath the fallen leaves, moss and litter of a woodland and much of the secret life of fungi is still unknown. Many of them supply a coating of mycelium threads round the roots of trees, especially conifers. This is known as the mycorrhizal layer, and it is an arrangement which is beneficial both to the trees and the fungi themselves, but there is still a great deal to learn about their growth and activities.

Toad and fungus 'Toadstool' is a term which has been used indiscriminately to cover many different kinds of mushroom-shaped fungi which are generally considered inedible. The name has no scientific basis at all and although it is possible to find a toad sitting beside, or even on top of a toadstool, it will have been attracted there, not by the fungus itself, but by the various insects which certainly are interested in fungi as a source of food for both adults and grubs. Slugs and snails and many of the higher animals, including squirrels, rabbits, deer and cattle also find many fungi palatable.

Left
Clitocybe infundibuliformis Superficially this fungus looks a little like a chanterelle, but it is much less solid and instead of being a uniform egg-yolk yellow, the gills on the under surface are almost white. The thin flesh is rather tough and although not poisonous, it is certainly not worth eating. A group of these fungi make a pretty picture in woods and on heaths, often half buried in moss, leaf litter or grass. They first appear in mid-summer and go on until autumn.

Below
Cortinarius elatior This attractive member of the large *Cortinarius* group of fungi appears in woodlands in the autumn, most usually under beeches, but also, as in this picture, under oaks. When it is quite young the edge of the cap is joined to the stalk by fine cobweb-like strands, which disappear as the cap expands. Both the cap and the stalk are slimy to the touch and the broad gills become a rusty violet colour in maturity. The stalk tapers both at the top and the bottom and often has a bluish tinge. The skin at the edge of the cap becomes rather wrinkled and grooved with age.

Opposite
Wood Puff Ball (*Lycoperdon pyriformae*) The puff ball family is a large one, but this is the only species that always grows on wood, either on old rotting stumps or arising from buried roots. The little pear-shaped fungi, often clustering in a large mass together, appear in mid-summer and are at first creamy-white and covered with coarse, mealy granules, which can be rubbed off. They gradually turn darker and become grey or yellowish-brown. Finally the skin begins to buckle, and the tops of the fungi open to release the innumerable spores which are scattered by the wind.

Left
Magpie fungus *(Coprinus picaceus)* No other fungus looks quite like this relative of the Lawyer's Wig, whose dark brown, tall cap is flecked with the white remains of the enveloping 'veil' which covers the young fungus as it emerges from the ground. It appears in autumn, in deciduous woods on rich land, and like all the *Coprinus* family is rather shortlived. The cap soon splits at the edges, and the gills which at first are white, turn quite black. The thin stalk is white and has no ring. It is rather rare and makes an interesting find on an autumn walk, although it is not edible.

Below

Coprinus niveus Another member of the same family, this pure white, rather small fungus springs from cow dung or horse manure any time during the summer and is quite common. The cap is egg-shaped at first, then opens up like a bell, goes black underneath, begins to curl at the edges and finally autodigests and dissolves away in the same way as the Lawyer's Wig. It is interesting to note its rapid appearance and disappearance. It is much too fragile to be used for cooking.

Opposite top and below

Coprinus micaceus and Coprinus sylvaticus There is a good deal of resemblance between these two related fungi, but while the former springs from old tree stumps or decaying roots, the latter grows in rich clay soils in woods. Both gradually spread out their bell-shaped caps, which darken as they age, but while *Coprinus sylvaticus* is auto-digesting, *Coprinus micaceus* does not dissolve away to the same extent. In both species the cap is grooved so as to appear finely pleated and if you look at the thin stems through a magnifying glass you will see that they are covered in fine downy hairs. When young the cap of *Coprinus micaceus* is sprinkled with little glistening mica-like scales, but these disappear later when the cap becomes dark in colour.

Below left
Hygrophorus conicus Among the many colourful late summer fungi this beautiful species, with its wavy, conical cap, is outstandingly attractive. The beautiful orange-red colour darkens with age and if the cap is bruised it turns black. It is not a real woodland fungus, but is more likely to be found on heaths and in meadows or in open, grassy woodland clearings and parks. It is only of medium size, the cap growing to 5 centimetres (2 inches) across and the yellow stalk reaching a height of 7 or 8 centimetres (3-3¼ inches).

Below right
Hygrophorus calyptiformis A relative of *Hygrophorus conicus*, but much rarer, this is another grassland fungus of attractive appearance. The pinky-mauve cap splits and flares with age looking like the swirling skirt of a ballet dancer. The gills forming the petticoats are pure white and the stalk a delicate grey-blue. A feast for the eyes but not worth eating.

Opposite top
Soap-scented Toadstool (*Tricholoma saponaceum*) If the smell of kitchen soap

can be considered a scent, then the name of this fungus is certainly very apt, and it also has a distinct soapy taste which makes it unfit for table. The specimen in the photograph is an old one which has been affected by the weather to such an extent that its normally uniformly dark grey cap has split all over to show the white beneath. The well spaced gills are also white, or faintly yellowish. It grows during late summer both in deciduous and coniferous woodlands.

45

Below

Coprinus disseminatus This delightful, dainty little fungus, which always grows in large quantities on or around decaying stumps of deciduous trees, gives the impression of a crowd of fairy children, all with similar blond bobbed hair covering their faces. The tiny caps are a fraction of an inch high and turn grey as they age. This happens in a matter of days and very soon the entire mass will have shrivelled and disappeared.

Opposite top
Cow Boletus *(Boletus bovinus)* Although
the *Boletus* family contains some of the
best of all edible fungi, it also has
several members which are either not
worth eating or unpleasant in taste. The
Cow Boletus, shown here growing
together with the odd, fan-shaped
Thelophora terrestris, which also favours
rather poor heathland or conifer woods,
is one of these. The slimy buff-coloured
cap, tinged with red, turns up at the
edges when the fungus becomes old, and
the yellow spore tubes run some way
down the stalk. The large pores divide up
into smaller tubes below the surface, and
the stalk narrows at the base.

Opposite below
Boletus variegatus A medium-sized fungus
with a scaly cap, which is unusual among
the *Boletus* group. It grows to 12 centimetres (5 inches) across and becomes
slimy in wet weather. The tubes are pale
at first, but become brownish-olive with
age and turn bluish when bruised, as can
be seen in the photograph. It grows
mainly in coniferous woods, especially
under pine trees on poor, sandy soils. It
can be eaten, but the taste is faintly
unpleasant – like chlorinated water.

Above
Boletus impolitus Appearing much earlier
than most other *Boletus* fungi, on chalky
soil and at the edges of beech woods, this
fungus offends by its unpleasant smell.
The cap is the colour of clay and the
porous layer on the underside is yellow,
sometimes with a tinge of orange. The
stalk is often flushed with red. The flesh
is creamy-white and solid but the smell
does not recommend it for kitchen use.

Above
Boletus luridus This could be mistaken at first glance for *Boletus edulis*, but on closer inspection it shows some rather extraordinary colour schemes which make it quite distinctive. There is a network of red veins, like those on a weather beaten face, all over the stout yellowish stalk, and when the fungus is mature the tubes underneath are green, with orange-red pores. If the tubes are peeled off the flesh is seen to be purplish-red underneath and it turns a somewhat lurid blue on cutting. Although it looks dangerous, it is not poisonous, but neither is it worth eating.

Opposite top
Helvella crispa This curiously crumpled and distorted looking fungus is related to the morels and can be found both in spring and autumn. It usually grows in deciduous woods on rich soil, often along the edges of footpaths. The flavour is nothing special and unless it is well boiled and rinsed the helvellic acid it contains is likely to cause trouble. On the whole it is best avoided and regarded as a curiosity rather than as potential food.

Opposite below
Verdigris agaric (*Stropharia aeruginosa*)

Although it sometimes grows in woods, this rather small fungus is more common in fields and pastures, or even in gardens, from mid-summer to early autumn. The blue-green cap is very slimy and when young it is sprinkled round the edge with little soft white scales, which later disappear. The blue-green stalk has a ring and below this it is covered in white scales. With age the fungus becomes a more yellowish green. The flesh is also green and smells rather like radishes. The gills are brown. It is not recommended for eating.

Above
Panaeolus semi-ovatus This small bell-shaped fungus grows on cow dung in pastures, or on richly manured ground. The cap, which is glossy and viscid, varies in colour from grey to the tan colour of the specimen in the picture. The gills are a mottled grey and finally turn black. The straight stem has a membraneous ring. A closely related species, *Panaeolus sphinctrinus*, also growing on dung, has a cap which is black when wet, and lead grey when dry. This is the 'teonanacatl' or sacred fungus which the Mexicans were already employing as an hallucinatory drug at the time of the Spanish invasion. Its use causes premature senility.

Opposite
Sulphur Tuft (*Hypholoma fasciculare*) This is another tree stump fungus and can be found at any time of the year on all kinds of old stumps, including those of conifers. The pale yellow caps gradually darken a little towards the centre and the thin yellow stems become slightly brownish towards the base. The gills are greenish-yellow at first and finally turn dark brown. If a cap is picked and put under a bowl on a piece of white paper it will be seen that the spores which drop down are very dark, almost blackish-purple in colour. The flesh is always yellow and has a very bitter taste.

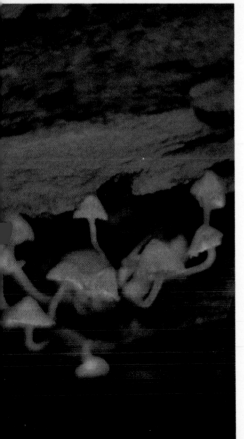

Above
Red Milk Cap *(Lactarius rufus)* In
Scandinavia this is known as the pepper
fungus because of its very strong peppery
taste which does not even disappear on
boiling. It always grows in pine woods in
late summer. There is usually a little knob
in the centre of the cap. The gills are
slightly paler than the cap and stalk and
when the fungus is broken a white milk
oozes out of the flesh. Although it is used
as a flavouring in some countries it is
likely to spoil a mushroom dish.

Left
Poromycena manipularis This is a rather
fragile little fungus, found in the forests
of Malaysia, where it grows on rotting
wood. At night it is distinctly luminous
and can even be photographed by its own
light. This picture was taken with the
addition of red torch light, in order to
show the background of the fallen tree
trunk on which the fungus is growing.
The light produced by the fungus itself is
greenish-yellow and is emitted from the
whole plant, including the stem and the
gills. Tropical forests are richer in
luminous fungi than the woods in more
temperate climates.

Opposite top
Cortinarius cinnabarinus This completely
red, rather dry little fungus also smells as
well as tastes of radishes and is not
generally regarded as edible, although it
is not likely to cause anything worse than
indigestion. It belongs to a large group of
fungi, many of which are very difficult
to distinguish from each other. This one
grows principally in beech woods,
appearing in early autumn, and it adds a
pleasing note of unusual colour among
the tawny autumn leaves.

Opposite below
The Sickener *(Russula emetica)* Among
the many *Russulas*, this one should
certainly be avoided. It grows most
commonly under conifers, although the
picture was taken in a mixed woodland.
The rather brittle cap is always a bright
red, the gills and stalk pure white, and
like all the *Russulas* it seems to be very
palatable to snails. The skin of the cap
peels off very easily and the flesh
underneath is reddish. The taste is very
acrid and although it is not a dangerous
fungus, it often causes vomiting if eaten.

Strange and sinister fungi

Fungi take so many forms and have such varied habits that it is not surprising that a good many of them were for a long time not recognized as fungi at all and probably many more still have not been correctly identified. Neither humans nor animals are immune from fungus infections. Troubles such as ringworm and athlete's foot are caused by fungi and so is aspergillosis, an infection of the lungs due to a very common mould which occurs everywhere. Many people are allergic to mould spores and that is one of the reasons why hay fever and asthma sufferers often get a second attack of their unpleasant symptoms in the autumn long after grasses and other plants have finished flowering. A peculiar and deadly fungus which has caused great havoc among both animals and humans in Europe in the past is Ergot, *Claviceps purpurea.* This does not infect humans directly but attacks grain, especially rye, and if this is then milled for flour or fed to livestock, it produces a serious and often deadly disease known as ergotism. Infected grains become very elongated and swollen, flesh coloured at first and then blackish purple. When they fall to the ground small fruiting bodies with curving stalks and small round heads appear and the spores produced by these infect the flowers of grasses and cereals again the following year. The symptoms of ergotism are either gangrene or convulsions and many serious epidemics have occurred, even in this century. Ergot does, however, also have medicinal uses and is actually cultivated for the extraction of the important alkaloids it contains.

The *Cordyceps* fungi, one of which is pictured in this chapter, are all insect parasites. Some of them specialize in moths, others in wasps or beetles, and one member of the family always attacks flies. There is also another quite different fungus which sometimes appears on adult flies crawling on the windowpanes. It shows itself as a white mouldy growth which finally covers the whole insect and then spreads a white powder of spores all around it. In some seasons it is very common, especially in late summer and early autumn.

Coral spot, *Nectria cinnabarina*, which appears as little pink pustules on old pea sticks and bean poles, is also a fungus, and is closely related to *Nectria galligena*, a far more damaging fungus as it attacks living trees, particularly apples, causing canker which can kill a tree in a few years. The so-called silver leaf disease, which affects plum and damson trees, is another insidious fungus. Strangely enough the peculiar silvery look of the leaves, which is one of the symptoms, is not caused directly by the fungus at all and no part of the mycelium ever enters the leaves, but the metabolism of the tree is upset and silvery air spaces appear in the leaves. The fruiting body, which is more or less lilac coloured, looks very like a bracket fungus and appears on the trunk or branches of the tree and the wood is stained a reddish-brown colour.

A tremendous number of plant diseases are caused by fungi, whose spores are always present in the air. Rust and blackspot on roses, mildews, moulds, rots and scabs of many different kinds are all due to similar causes and most of the diseases are incurable. The only way to deal with them is to keep the foliage of the plants covered with fungicide sprays which prevent the spores from growing when they do land on their host plants. Some of these fungus troubles are inhibited by impurities in the air and that is one of the reasons why roses in industrial and urban areas where air pollution is high, suffer much less from blackspot than those which grow in the country.

Wherever man makes and builds in the world, fungi are there too, waiting for their opportunity to attack his handiwork, and the dry rot fungus described in this chapter is one of the most destructive of all. At one time it was a major headache for the Navy, causing temporarily unused ships to rot away at their moorings when they were left for some time with the hatches closed. People living in old houses built without damp courses have to be constantly vigilant against this fungus, and leaking gutters, dripping taps, cracked roof tiles and blocked ventilators under the floors can all very quickly cause trouble which may go unnoticed if a house stands empty for some time. The deterioration of so many houses, especially in poorer areas where the householders cannot afford to do regular repairs, is to a very large extent due to dry rot. The only real defence against this fungus is to keep all woodwork permanently dry. Oak and cedar woods are more resistant to attack than the usual timber of spruce and pine, and impregnation with creosote will make any timber rot-proof for a great number of years.

The unpleasant Stinkhorn fungus noted for its rapid appearance and unpleasant smell, is also illustrated in this chapter. It is a common fungus and so is the smaller Dog Stinkhorn, which has an orange-red tip to its stalk. This becomes visible when the flies have cleared away the spore mass. A much rarer and

more spectacular relation of these fungi is *Clathrus ruber*. When fully expanded it looks like a coral red ball of lattice work sitting on the ground, but few people with a sense of smell can bear to be near it for very long. It puts the Stinkhorn in the shade, both for appearance and odour, and flies gather round it in swarms. It begins, like the Stinkhorn, as a round white 'egg' and when this cracks the red lattice structure expands so rapidly that one can see it happen.

Fungi of this type are known as phalloids and different species are found all over the world. In the genus *Lysurus* the stalk bears five to seven separate arms which are orange or red. They are most probably natives of Australia and have been introduced to Europe and even to America with imported produce. Many of the specimens have been found near rubbish dumps or in gardens where imported plants have been grown.

Asterophora parasitica Big fleas have little fleas and some of the larger fungi are apt to be attacked in old age by smaller parasitic species which hasten their decay. One of these is shown here, sprouting just below the cap of an aged *Russula*. All the *Russulas* are liable to suffer in this way and so are the *Lactarius* species. The little *Asterophora* has a cap which is white at first, covered in silky fibres, and later turns a pale grey. The gills on the underside very quickly become covered in a thick brown powdering of spores. The parasites usually appear in clusters and have a sickeningly unpleasant smell.

Left
Chlorosplenium aeruginosum It is not
unusual to find pieces of wood which are
stained an attractive blue-green colour
and the agent responsible is this small
fungus whose mycelium penetrates fallen
branches or broken trunks of several
trees, but mainly oak. In many cases
there is no sign of the small fruiting
bodies at all but if they do appear it is in
the autumn and they are quite tiny, only
half a centimetre across the caps. The
stained wood was much valued in the
nineteenth century when it was used in
the manufacture of various inlaid wooden
objects, known as Tunbridge ware.

Opposite top
Orange Peel Fungus (*Peziza aurantia*)
This brightly coloured and well named
woodland fungus often grows in such
crowded groups that the individual cup-
shaped structures become distorted and
buckled. It first appears in late summer
and often lasts until the end of the year.
The smooth inner surface is the exact
colour of orange peel, and the outside is
covered in a layer of white down. It crops
up on lawns and garden paths and on
more or less bare soil in mixed woods.
The gay colouring distinguishes it from
various other cup fungi of the same
group, but it might be confused with
Peziza rutilans which is a typical
heathland fungus and much smaller.

Opposite below left
Cordyceps militaris This is another
parasitic fungus which attacks both
caterpillars and chrysalids of moths,
usually those which either feed in the soil
as larvae or burrow underground to
pupate. The whole insect becomes filled
with a mass of white fungus threads and
finally the fruiting body, which looks like
a slim, slightly crooked, orange finger,
appears on the surface. There are many
kinds of *Cordyceps* and the first to be
described was *Cordyceps chinensis* which
used to be common in Peking and is
valued in China for medicinal purposes.
Certain tropical species of *Cordyceps* may
grow over a foot high.

Opposite below right
Tremella mesenterica This crumpled,
orange-yellow gelatinous fungus belongs
to the same group as the edible Jew's Ear.
It grows on dead trunks or branches of
deciduous trees, especially in late autumn.
At first it is soft and rather slimy but with
age it dries and hardens and becomes
much darker in colour. It is sometimes
called Witches' Butter and this name is
also used for another somewhat similar
fungus, *Exidia glandulosa*, which is dark
brown or black in colour and grows
principally on oak. A third species,
Tremella foliacea, which is pinkish-brown
or slightly violet, prefers the stumps of
pine trees.

Top
Bird's Nest Fungus (*Cyathus olla*) These strange little fungi, of which there are several species, grow on dead twigs, straws, fir cones, beechmast or even sometimes directly on the ground. They are shaped like shallow cups or inverted cones, and sometimes have a finely fluted interior. The cup is at first covered by a thin skin, but later this breaks away and reveals a varying number of more or less oval-shaped bodies lying inside the cup, just like eggs in a miniature birds' nest. These are not outsize spores, but only spore containers. Heavy rain drops bounce them out of the cups and in time the outer skin breaks and the spores are set free.

Below
Staghorn fungus (*Calocera viscosa*) An autumn and winter fungus, very pretty and bright and slightly slimy to the touch, usually growing on the stumps of conifers. If dried it becomes hard and horny and somewhat darker and as it has no unpleasant smell it is sometimes used as a decoration in a bowl of moss. A related kind, unbranched and paler in colour, grows on deciduous wood. The so-called Fairy Clubs, which are often profusely branched, belong to a different family. Some of these are poisonous and as it is difficult to identify them with accuracy they are best left alone.

Opposite top
Earth Star (*Geastrum triplex*) This strange fungus is fairly common under beech trees in autumn and also grows under other kinds of deciduous trees. When it first appears above ground it looks rather like a pale pinky-brown onion sitting among the leaves, but after a while the thick outermost layer splits and curls back to form a star-shaped border to the inner layer which is grey and still retains an onion-like shape. Finally a little hole, fringed with silky hairs, appears at the top of the 'bulb' and the myriads of spores escape in much the same way as they do from a puff ball. The spent fungus dries and shrivels and is sometimes blown about by the wind.

Opposite below
Geastrum fornicatum If ever you should see some dark little knob-shaped heads peering at you through the undergrowth beneath deciduous trees, you are not being watched by 'little men' of the woods, but have come upon a rare and local fungus, related to the Earth Star. As it ripens the outer layer splits into four separate sections which bend back and push the spore-filled 'head' upwards to a height of about 10 centimetres (4 inches). Because of the likeness to a small human figure this fungus was named *Fungus anthropomorphus* when it was first described in 1688.

Top
Slime fungus *(Fuligo septica flava)* The slime fungi are a very primitive family and this fairly common example varies in colour from creamy white to yellow. It grows both on old stumps and on the ground, often among grasses and resembles nothing so much as a plateful of rice pudding which somebody has decided to throw away. The fungus feeds on bacteria and changes its shape and outline as it grows and spreads. There is no separate cap or stalk; the whole fungus is just a rather soft, moist and slimy mass of cells.

Middle
Dry rot fungus *(Merulius lacrymans)* This most sinister fungus can also be detected by its smell, even when it is hiding under the floor boards and doing its frightening damage out of sight. It is a serious menace in damp houses, particularly in old and neglected buildings, lacking in ventilation. It spreads with terrifying rapidity, often covering large areas of floors and walls with its revolting fruiting bodies, which exude drops of moisture. Dry rot feeds on wood, causing it to crumble and crack and once it gains a hold it is very difficult to eradicate. It can even pass through dividing walls by means of long tough grey strands which penetrate the bricks.

Below
Cramp Balls *(Daldinia concentrica)* Once believed to be a cure for cramp, this parasitic fungus is normally found growing on the trunks or larger branches of ash trees. At first it is a dark reddish-brown colour, but when fully ripe it becomes quite black and shiny. This burnt appearance has given it the popular name of King Alfred's Cakes. The fungus grows quite quickly during the autumn and remains on the tree until the following summer. If it is cut through with a knife, the inside is seen to be marked with alternating darker and lighter rings, like the flesh of a beetroot. The spores are produced in the summer and are always discharged at night, and because the fungus can store water, the process will continue for a long time even if it is removed from the tree and kept dry.

Opposite
Fairy Clubs *(Clavaria fusiformis)* The fairy club fungi vary considerably in their shape and colour. Many of them are branched and very much resemble some types of coral. The one shown here is of a simpler type and usually quite plain, although occasionally one or two of the 'clubs' in a cluster may have two sections. They are often flattened and bent or twisted. There is no cap, and the spores are formed on the outside of the hollow fruiting body. Fairy clubs nearly always grow in the open, in meadows and fields or on heaths and moorland, among heather and moss.

Top left
Coprinus lagopus This 'Slim Jim' of a
fungus, which is nearly always found
growing all alone, belongs to the same
family as the Lawyer's wig. It does not
digest itself to the same extent, but
instead it rolls back the edge of its cap, so
that it is finally turned almost completely
inside out, and the gills disappear, leaving
only slight ridges behind. In early youth
the fungus is narrowly egg-shaped and
covered in white hairs, which soon darken
and then drop off. The white stalk always
remains hairy, especially on the lower
portions. It grows among leaf litter in
deciduous woods and appears throughout
the summer.

Top right
Battarea phalloides This rare fungus,
which is only found very occasionally in
sandy places, was first discovered in
Suffolk, England in 1784, but since then
it has turned up in various localities in
England and in a few places on the

continent of Europe. It develops from an
egg-shaped body known as a volva, buried
several inches deep in the ground, and
very rapidly sends up a tall, tapering stalk,
covered in rough brown fibres and looking
rather like a miniature pine trunk. The
small head of the fungus is brown, and as
it rises, carries with it, like a skull cap,
the torn-off top of the volva, which
gradually dries and shrivels. The spores
are formed inside the head, as in a puff
ball, and are then released when the skin
splits along the rim.

Opposite top
Stinkhorn (*Phallus impudicus*) The strong
smell of carrion which sometimes assails
the nostrils in gardens and woods during
the summer and autumn is quite likely to
emanate from this highly unpleasant and
aptly named fungus. Although it is often
hidden in the undergrowth its smell
always gives it away. Starting as a white
'egg' it develops in a matter of hours,
sending up a white hollow stalk tipped

with a ridged cap covered in a dark olive
spore-bearing jelly whose powerful odour
attracts flies from afar. They feed on the
jelly and thus distribute the spores and
when the fungus has been made clean
and white it no longer stinks, but soon
decays. It usually springs up year after
year in the same place.

Opposite below
Ergot (*Claviceps purpurea*) This curious
fungus is a parasite on grasses, and more
rarely on cereals, particularly rye. It
causes the infected grains to become
enlarged, swollen, and dark in colour as
well as highly poisonous. If infected grain
or grasses are fed to cattle, or made into
flour for human consumption, it gives
rise to a serious disease called ergotism.
This has often happened in the past in
countries where rye was the principal
cereal crop and the danger of the infected
grains was not understood. Drugs derived
from ergot are used in obstetrics to
produce contractions of the womb.

Bracket fungi

These fungi grow in woodlands and forests all over the world, and although they differ considerably from each other in appearance they are, with few exceptions, always found growing on wood. Many of them attack living trees, their spores gaining access through wounds caused by wind damage, or injuries inflicted by man, animals, birds or insects. One of the reasons why tree surgeons always carefully seal any wounds caused by lopping branches is to prevent the entry of fungi of this sort as well as other types which attack growing timber.

The damage caused varies with the kind of bracket fungus which is responsible. Some of them produce what is known as heart rot, right in the centre of the tree, causing it eventually to become hollow. A tree may seem outwardly sound but if it is felled for timber it is useless and only fit for firewood. The damage also impairs the tree's resistance to gales, and although such a tree may remain alive for a long time, even in its sick condition, it is apt to fall unexpectedly in a high wind. The majority of ancient oaks are more or less hollow in the centre because of the activities of fungi of this kind. They are not strictly speaking parasitic, because the central core of wood in a growing tree no longer consists of living cells, and after the tree falls the fungi may continue with their destruction of the timber. They often produce a characteristic staining of the wood, which varies in colour with different species. The Beef Steak fungus, for example, colours oak-timber brown. The *polyporus fungus*, which grows on birches, attacks not the heart wood but the so-called sap wood which lies just under the bark and contains the living cells which convey nourishment from the roots to the branches, and there are other fungi which act in the same way. This is far more serious damage of a parasitic nature and a tree attacked by this type of fungus usually dies fairly quickly. Wounds in the bark are the most usual point of entry and trees which have been bruised and battered in one way or another are the most apt to suffer. Damage on building sites where a few amenity trees have been left standing unprotected, cuts caused by grass-cutting machines mowing too close to the trunks, vandalism, wounding by chafing wire ties and the thoughtless carving of initials into the bark can all be responsible for opening a door to fungi. The Dutch Elm disease is caused by a different type of fungus, not of the bracket family, which gains entry through the holes bored by small bark beetles. An association between insects and fungi is in fact quite common and wood-boring grubs and beetles often feed on fungi growing in their tunnels.

A large number of bracket fungi grow not on living wood but only on dead timber, especially on old tree stumps and on tree trunks and branches which have fallen to the ground. They also attack newly-felled timber, and when this is left lying out of doors, without any treatment to preserve it, it may become infected very quickly. It is well known that timber completely immersed in water will remain sound for extremely long periods, provided it is not attacked by marine worms, but all timber exposed to the air will sooner or later succumb to fungus infection.

Although bracket fungi bear a family resemblance they do vary tremendously both in size, colour and appearance. Most of them have a layer of tubes on the underside, but in some cases the spore-producing area is pleated into gills. When young, they are frequently quite soft and pliable, even occasionally edible, but as they age they become more tough and leathery and many of them end up by being as hard as the wood on which they grow, and the upper surface may have the consistency of hardened resin or lacquer.

The fruiting bodies of some of the softer species, such as the yellow and the brown *Grifolias*, only last for a few months, while others are perennial and may remain in position for years, growing bigger and bigger and adding one layer after another of spore-bearing tubes. More than twenty layers have on occasion been counted, where an old bracket has been allowed to remain undisturbed. When the spores are shed, they fall down in astronomical numbers in some instances, staining both the fungus itself and the surroundings with the coloured dust.

Some bracket fungi are so spongy that the water can be squeezed out of them as from a bath sponge; certain species 'weep' drops of moisture without even being touched. It is usual for a number of separate fruiting bodies to appear at the same time, often close together and arranged in tiers like starched frills on a dress, or undulating shelves or wall brackets. It is of course this habit which has given them their popular name. The colouring ranges from pure white to charcoal and quite a number of them are most beautifully marked and coloured, with contrasting edges and a velvety texture.

Their effect on the wood on which they are growing varies. Some break it up into regular cubes

or blocks, others separate the fibres from each other or cause a general softening and crumbling of the timber. If the wood on which they are growing is cut open, the mycelial strands can be seen inside it, and if the fungi are left to do their work the wood will eventually disintegrate. It is not unusual for several different fungi to be at work simultaneously on the same piece of wood, or else one follows the other. If the attack has proceeded far enough to cause real damage nothing can be done to save the timber from destruction, but in the early stages soaking in preservative or heat treatment can be used to kill the fungus and stop the rot.

Coltrichia perennis Although included in the bracket fungus group, this does not grow on trees and is, in fact, shaped like a wide cup or wine glass on a short stem. The edge is often wavy and split and the inner surface is attractively marked in concentric rings of alternate dark and light brown, changing to grey in the middle. In young specimens the entire surface is covered in fine silky down. The short tubes underneath run some way down the stalk and have very tiny pores. They are dull greyish-yellow at first and then turn brown. The fungus grows on poor sandy soil and often appears after fires. It is found all the year round.

Left

Grifolia sulphurea This is one of the larger bracket fungi, sometimes becoming 40 centimetres (18 inches) across; it may grow in a composite mass, as in the photograph, or form a single spreading fan. The upper surface is more or less orange-yellow, becoming tan coloured with age, and the lower surface is a pale sulphur colour. The yellow flesh is thick and spongy and has an unpleasant sour smell as well as a nasty taste. It causes serious decay of oak trees and will also attack some conifers. It is a summer fungus, appearing throughout the season.

Below

Ganoderma applanatum This is a typical bracket fungus, growing on a number of different trees, but principally on beech, causing great damage through heart rot. It is perennial and reaches quite a large size. The upper surface is very bumpy and uneven, almost rock hard, with a wavy edge, and either grey or reddish-brown in colour. The spore layer on the under side is white when young, but later becomes light brown. A huge quantity of brown spores is produced, which frequently stains the trunk of the tree and the bracket itself. In the photograph the red-brown dust can be clearly seen.

Opposite top

Fomes fomentarius Sometimes confused with *Ganoderma applanatum*, this bracket is much more grey in colour when mature and the spores are white instead of brown. The upper surface is at first softly velvety but later feels quite hard, and the whole fungus becomes very thick as annual layers of spore tubes develop. In America and on the continent of Europe it attacks many different trees including beech, maple and poplar, but in Britain it is found mainly in Scotland and nearly always on birches. In the past this fungus was used for the manufacture of a kind of tinder known as amadou.

Opposite below

Phaeolus schweinitzii Very striking looking, sometimes with a thick central stalk and a top covered in a dense woolly brown fur, this bracket fungus usually attacks pines, growing either on the base of the trunk or on the roots. The large, rather angular and irregular pores are yellow at first and later become darker. The flesh is spongy and full of water and the spores are white. A great deal of harm can be done to pine timber by this fungus which causes the wood to break up into brown cubical blocks.

Top left
Trametes confragasa (rubescens) This
might be taken as a classic example of a
bracket fungus, the thin semicircular
brackets looking just like a series of very
neat shelves fixed to the trunk of a
decaying tree. In this fungus the upper
surface, with a velvety texture, is always
more or less reddish-brown or pinkish in
colour, with distinct lighter and darker
zones. The white tubes of the under
surface show along the smooth, only
slightly wavy edge. It grows on many
different kinds of deciduous wood and
the fruiting bodies nearly always appear
in this manner, in a long row one above
the other.

Top right
Gloeoporus adustus An all-year-round
bracket fungus which usually grows in
very crowded masses on fallen trunks or

old stumps, or on felled timber which has
been left lying about in the woods. It
normally attacks only deciduous wood.
The brownish-grey upper surface is like
very short, dense fur, the wavy edge is
white and the minute pores on the
underside are white at first but eventually
become black. A thin, but distinct layer
of a black, jelly-like substance separates
the tubes from the flesh of the bracket
and can be seen clearly if the fungus is
cut through. Attacked timber develops
curious white flecks in the sap wood.

Opposite below left
Piptoporus betulinus Confined exclusively
to birches, both living and dead, this very
solid bracket fungus starts off by being
almost flat and pure white, with an
incurved edge. As it ages, it begins to
bulge, and the top becomes grey-brown
but remains quite smooth. The flesh is

firm and white and quite moist in young
specimens, but later on its consistency
becomes very like cork. It has long been
used by entomologists for mounting
small insects in display cabinets and is
generally referred to simply as *polyporus*.

Opposite below right
Trametes versicolor This is a most
attractive looking, rather thin bracket
fungus, growing on many kinds of dead
timber. The wavy surface has a soft velvet
pile and is very variable in colour, usually
some shade of brown, but may contain
yellow, grey, green or even blue zones.
The contrasting white pores, visible along
the edge, give the fungus a most elegant
appearance. Occasionally the entire
bracket develops upside down, so that it
looks entirely white or very pale yellow.
It is present all the year round, but never
grows on living trees.

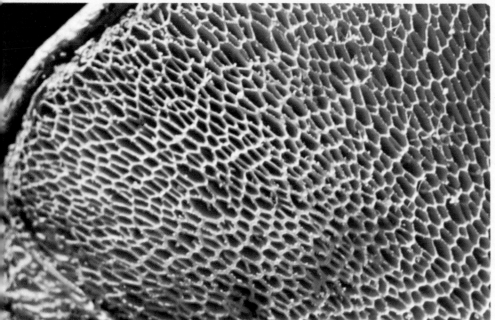

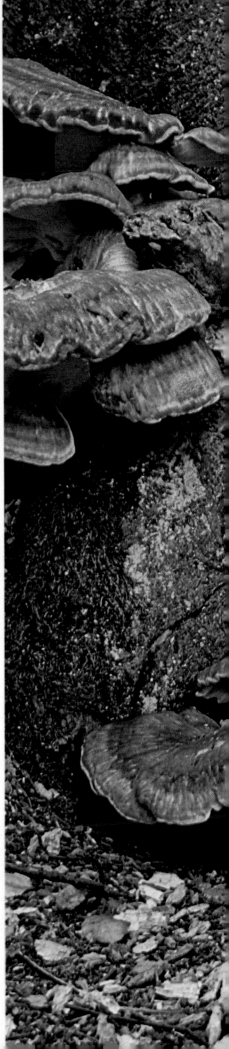

Top and above
Dryad's Saddle *(Polyporus squamosus)*
This handsome fungus, which sometimes
measures 30 centimetres (1 foot)
across, usually grows on elm trees, but it
may also be found on maple, oak and
various other deciduous trees. Its presence
denotes an unhealthy state, and it causes
a white rot of the wood. The underside
of the cap is covered in rather coarse,
white pores and the scaly top often bends
and curves, giving the fungus very much
the shape of a saddle. It has a peculiar,
sweet smell and an unpleasant taste.

Opposite
Grifolia gigantea The largest of the
bracket fungi, sometimes forming a
cluster measuring up to a metre (39
inches). The tops are fan shaped, often
overlapping each other, brown and
covered with small scales with white
pores on the underside, which turn black
if they are bruised. While young the

fungus is quite brittle and easily broken,
but later it becomes tough and leathery.
It appears in late summer or early autumn
near the base of tree trunks, especially on
oaks and beeches, and lasts through the
autumn and early winter. Like *Grifolia
sulphurea* it has a sour smell.

Overleaf
Grifolia frondosa More common in North
America than in Europe, this large,
compound bracket fungus is known in
Canada as 'The Hen of the Woods'. The
rather narrow, grey-brown or yellowish-
brown, wrinkled, overlapping and
semicircular caps are very reminiscent of
the fluffed-up feathers of a broody hen
who has just been disturbed on the nest.
The fungus grows at the base of
deciduous trees, especially oaks, during
the autumn. The mycelium persists from
year to year and forms a large mass in
the soil. It also penetrates tree roots
and trunks, causing a white rot.

Acknowledgments

The publishers would like to thank the following organizations and individuals for their kind permission to reproduce the pictures in this book:

H R Allen (Natural History Photographic Agency) 2-3; 8 left and right; 11 top; 13; 21 bottom left; 41; 43 bottom; 45 bottom; 47; 52 top; 66 top; 67 bottom

Arthur S Bailie 72

A W Brand (NHPA) 23 top right; 30-31; 59 bottom

E G Burt (NHPA) 22; 23 top left; 31 bottom right and left; 44 right; 45 top; 49 top; 53 top; 55; 57 bottom left; 65

Stephen Dalton (NHPA) 39; 43 top; 70-71

Christine Foord (NHPA) 29 top
R G Foord (NHPA) 12 top; 60 middle
Brian Hawkes (NHPA) 11 bottom; 17; 18 top; 19; 21 bottom right; 29 bottom; 36; 37 top; 42 top and bottom; 44 left; 49 bottom; 50; 56; 57 bottom right; 59 top; 60 top and bottom; 62 right; 66 bottom; 67 top

G E Hyde (NHPA) 1; 5; 7; 9 top and bottom; 10 top; 12 bottom; 15 top left and top right; 14; 15 bottom; 20; 24; 24-25; 27 bottom left and bottom right; 27 top; 28; 33; 35 top; 40 top; 46 bottom; 48; 50-51; 57 top; 58 top and bottom; 61; 62 left; 63 top; 68-69; 69 bottom left and right

Dr Clinton Maccoy 21 top; 70 top and bottom

Walter J C Murray (NHPA) 18 bottom; 35 bottom

L H Newman (NHPA) 68 left

Ivan Polunin (NHPA) 52 bottom

S C Porter (NHPA) 63 bottom

M C F Proctor (NHPA) 23 bottom; 26; 40 bottom; 46 top; 53 bottom

Dr D A Reid (NHPA) 37 bottom

Trustees of the British Museum (Natural History) 34

G Wall (NHPA) 10 bottom

Case design by Gertude Hermes RA